The Magic of Mums

To my own magic mum.
And with love to Juliet, my awesome A-Z of everything
and mum to Joss, Woody and Rufus.

In loving memory of my magnificent mother-in-law, mother of nine,
Carole Chambers (1943-2019).
We miss you.

I am grateful for the generous assistance of the Society of Authors
in awarding me an Authors Foundation Grant to support the
writing of this book.

Justin Coe

In memory of my mum, Frances Wells (1935-2019).

Steve Wells

The Magic of Mums

Poems by
Justin Coe

Illustrations by
Steve Wells

Otter-Barry BOOKS

Contents

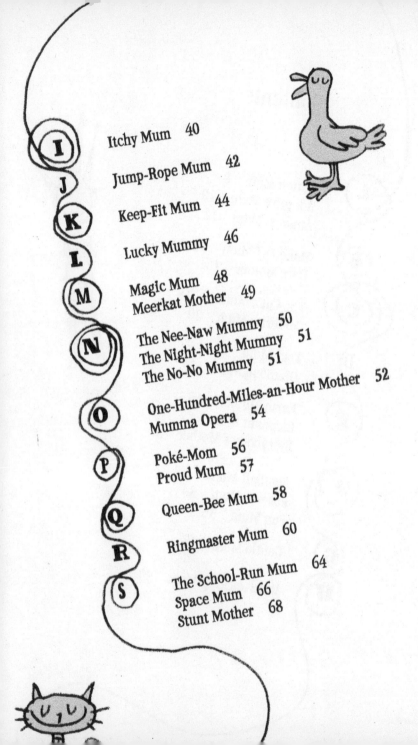

ACTION MUM

Action Man, please move over
You're nothing but a plastic poser
If there's a job that you need done
The one you want is **ACTION MUM**

Action Man might act all macho
But he's as much use as a statue
In a real-life crisis this 'brave soldier'
Would just play dead behind the sofa

While **ACTION MUM** will trudge through mud
Swim through tears and wade through blood
Just to reach her little baby
Just to lift her child to safety

Call on her – she'll come out fighting
You won't find her in a toy box hiding
Or chilling at some cool pool party
In the bath with Ken and Barbie

ACTION MUM will give no quarter
To those who'd harm her son or daughter
She'll beat the bullies – don't you doubt it
Before Action Man can change his outfit

And when the battles are all ended
There's one hero who'll be remembered
So, Action Man, put down your gun
You are no match for **ACTION MUM**.

ADOPTIVE MUM

Based on a true story

I'd just given birth to my babies
in the farmyard barn
when you came waddling over,
a lost little duckling
looking for her Mumma.
Any other morning I'd have eyed you up for breakfast,
but I wasn't feeling peckish
and *aww*, you did look so sweet.
Everyone needs a mummy, I thought.
What's another mouth to feed?

For sure, you were peculiar,
all fluff and no fur!
No paws, no claws, no teeth, no whiskers!
Only the strangest little beak and two rubbery feet!
You were nothing like any of your brothers or sisters.

Of course, the hens all cackled,
"Look at that cat mothering a duckling!
It's unnatural!"
And the farmer eyed me warily.
But I never would have hurt you
because at that moment you found me
it was only in my nature to nurture you.

Weeks later,
now you've taken to the water
and learned to quack,
you still
sometimes come back
to follow me round the fields.
The geese can honk with laughter all they like.
I wouldn't be without you.

I just don't understand the fuss.
Compared to the bond we share,
what difference could a bit of difference between us
make to us?

And listen,
I don't even care
if you grow up to be
a duck, a chicken, a goose or a pigeon,

I'll always be your mother duck
and you'll always be my kitten.

ANXIOUS MUM

Don't forget your toothbrush, darling,
take these crisps, in case you're starving.
I can't stand the panic of our parting.
Are you leaving me already?

You'll need money for emergencies
and remedies for allergies.
I expect you'll need a book to read...
And why not take your teddy?

What about some nice warm socks?
Sunscreen cream in case it's hot
and if it rains – a mackintosh...
Don't go without your slippers!

Your shoes are looking worse for wear,
why don't you pack another pair?
Quickly, let me brush your hair...
And here's some spare fresh knickers.

Be good, my darling, mind your language,
shall I make an extra sandwich?
And here's a plaster and a bandage
in case of injury.

All right, Mum, please do not stress,
I'm not heading for the wilderness,
it's just a normal day at my school desk
and I'll be home by half-past three!

BAKE-OFF MUM

Mum has a dream to be the queen
Of tarts and puds and pastries
A Bake-Off winner with every dinner
Or posh dessert she makes me

But however she tries to make her pies
And crêpes and cakes delicious
It all goes wrong and makes me long
For something less ambitious

The Rhubarb Scones and Orange Blancmange
She dished up were disgusting
Her Crème Brûlée and her Cheese Soufflé
We chucked them in the dustbin

Her Prinsesstårta was a palaver
Her Prune Pavlova best forgotten
I'm sad to report the Gooseberry Torte
Gave me a soggy bottom

So let's say goodbye to all her pies
Her tarts, bakes, cakes and quiches
What I'd love most is cheese on toast
And a tin of peaches!

BOSS MOTHER

She's the **GODMOTHER** –
  But she's no story-fairy
She's the **BOSS MOTHER** –
  When she's cross she's scary
In her shades and her suit she rocks
  the look of a gangsta
And you'd better beware the glare of her anger

She's the **GODMOTHER** –
  You've gotta respect her
She's my proud provider
  She's my chief protector
Even teachers cower from her power
  and majesty
And nobody dares to diss her family

She's the **GODMOTHER** –
  And I'm her precious princess
No other child has a chance in the Fancy-Dress
If my costume alone can't get me selected
Then the Godmother can cos she's
WELL-CONNECTED

She's the **BOSS MOTHER** –
  The chief of our clan
But if the law come for her
  She'll hold up her hands
And she'll tell them the truth…
  What she's guilty of
Is having nothing but a heart full of
  MUVVA LUV

THE CAT'S MOTHER

She fills his bowl to the brim with biscuits
And feeds him
Fresh chicken tit-bits
Straight from her finger-tips

She knows every swish of his tail
And every twitch of his whiskers
Attends to his every meow, yowl and hiss
And forgives him the unwanted 'gifts'
He sometimes slips into her slippers

In the evenings
She calls him home for cuddles
With her familiar tongue-clicks and whistles
And nuzzles up to him
Running the soft bristles
Of her brush
Against his fur
While he purrs
His love for her

He is her pet
Her darling
Her baby, her bubba

And she...
Well, who is she?
She's the cat's mother!

CELEBRITY MUM

I see her every day in the papers
I read her twitter updates and facebook status
She's got a million likes and a million haters

MY MUM'S A CELEBRITY

You can view our house in a magazine
I go to school in a limousine
Everyone knows that I'm living the dream

MY MUM'S A CELEBRITY

Every night's an invite to a party
We've got an open door to the paparazzi
They take my photo then push past me

MY MUM'S A CELEBRITY

I've got all the latest fancy gear
But sometimes the tension turns to tears
My friends are jealous but they've no idea

MY MUM'S A CELEBRITY

GET ME OUT OF HERE!

DAD-MUM

When you were born
I was a long-distance daddy,
always driving my lorry
late into the night.
I never let it worry me
how many miles there were between us.
As long as the wheels were turning
I was earning the money.

But if your mum could see us these days
she'd be amazed
at the dab hand I am now at the laundry,
or at the care I take to plait your hair,
or how we take the time each night
to share a story.

I know I do not have
a sparkle of your mother's magic.
I just cook the recipes
that keep her in our memories
and try to keep the house
as she would have it.

And because your mum
could never bear
to see you sad,
I do my best to love you
twice as much
for both of us,
be both
your mum and dad.

DIAMOND MUM

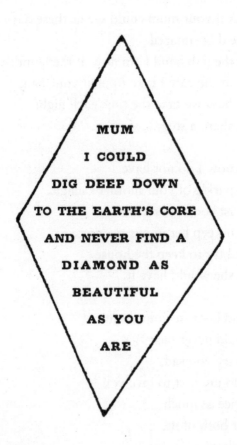

MUM
I COULD
DIG DEEP DOWN
TO THE EARTH'S CORE
AND NEVER FIND A
DIAMOND AS
BEAUTIFUL
AS YOU
ARE

EARTH MOTHER

Dear Mother Earth
You who gave birth to us
Nursed and nurtured us
You who gave us
Air to breathe
Water to drink
Food to eat
You who gifted us
Flowers, trees
Deep seas, cool rivers
Your creatures great and small
And the keys to all
Your hidden treasures

Please
Forgive us

For we have felled your forests
Poisoned your rivers
Polluted your sea and your sky

Now we are all in danger
We feel the heat of your anger

Excuse us Mother
All our neglect
All you ever asked for
Was a little respect

ELEPHANT MUM

How can I forget the day that you were born? For so long I'd carried you inside me, and then there you were. My wobbly-legged little elephant, who didn't know what to do with her trunk.

I remember feeding from your udder, Mumma. Glugging mouthfuls of milk every day!

I remember how, later, you would hold onto my tail with your trunk and we would walk with your aunts down to the watering hole.

I remember how I rolled in the mud and splashed you all with the mucky water!

I remember how I kept you close.

I remember how, if I ever strayed too far, you'd trumpet loudly and I'd come running. But one day...

I remember the men came with gunpowder.

I remember how I fell into their trap. And how, when you came after me they drove you back with their thunder. I remember many painful nights in chains and long exhausting days, carrying men and women on my back.

I remember many times I returned to look for you. Mothers and daughters should never part.

I remember one day other men and women came – kind men and women – and they led me gently back to the water. But I was still a lost and lonely wanderer. Until, at last, I heard your call.

I remember you running to me, me running to you,
our ears wide with excitement.

I remember how we joined trunks and I cried,
"Mumma, I thought you'd forgotten me" and with
your ears still flapping, you replied...

 "If I can remember my way to water did you think
I'd forget my daughter? Never forget that...

**ELEPHANTS
ALWAYS
REMEMBER!**

EVERYBODY'S MOTHER

My mother is everybody's mother
For her warmth and welcome she is well known
So budge up and make room for another
No child should be without a happy home

She has the wisest eyes that understand you
No matter where you've been or what you've done
Her house is a hug you can snuggle into
A comfort blanket to keep you warm

She takes us in – the bruised and the broken
The betrayed, waylaid and too afraid to care
Her heart, like her door, is always open
So many of us have found our refuge here

And though to each and every child she's Mum
She still makes me feel like I'm her only one.

31

FOOTBALL MUMS

soMEwhere in the crOwd that surrounds the Touchline she cHeers me on so loud and clear.

Even if she's hard to spot, she's not too hard to heaR

(To the tune of My Darling Clementine)
Oh my mother, how I love her
If I lost her I'd be sad
She can't half kick a football
She's better than your dad!

(To the tune of The Quartermaster's Store)
She's class, she's cool, she's always on the ball
My Mum, My Mum!
She's smart, she's fast, you couldn't get one past
My Mum, My Mum!

(To the tune of When Johnny Comes Marching Home)
Who's the goddess of this game?
My Mum, My Mum!
Everybody praise her name
My Mum, My Mum!
There's nothing that she cannot do
Makes Man United look like Crewe
My Mum, the best one that there is!

FOREVER MUM

You can tell me what you used to be
Show me photographs, I still won't see
Who that baby was on Granny's knee
And the pink-haired punk... just who was she?

Cos you'll always be a mum to me
You'll always be my Mummy

You can run away – but you won't get free
Leave house and home and lose the key
Escape to space or sail to sea
But any way you try to flee

You'll always be a mum to me
You'll always be my Mummy

You can tell me what you dreamed you'd be
Doctor, Dentist, VIP
Prime Minister, celebrity
Chat-show hostess on TV

But you'll always be a mum to me
You'll always be my Mummy

And as you grow old who knows maybe
You'll forget the name you chose for me
And when I visit you and bring your tea
You'll smile and ask – "Just who is he?"

But still you'll be a mum to me
You'll always be my Mummy

FUN MUM

Why should Dad have all the joy
Just because he is a boy?

I, too, can joke and laugh and play
As well as he does, any day

If I didn't have so many chores
I'd horse about on all fours

Or mould some mud into a pie
Or fly a kite up in the sky

Yes, why should Dad have all the fun?
Today you're going to play with Mum!

We're going to get out all the toys
Run around and make some noise

Feast on sweets and lots of fizzy
And dance about until we're dizzy

We'll go outside and blow some bubbles
And jump about in muddy puddles

Then back indoors we'll throw confetti
And wash our faces with spaghetti

After that we'll need to rest...
Dad can clean up all the mess

GENTLE MUM

Heart-listener, soft-whisperer
Tummy-tickler, giggle-giggler
Breakfast-baker, memory-maker
Fancy-dresser, birthday-blesser
Bubble-blower, party-thrower
Candle-lighter, joy-inviter
Play-explorer, peace-restorer
Nature-guider, truth-confider
Trouble-smoother, worry-soother
Wonder-wisher, goodnight-kisser

Thank you, you're a gentle-mum

HARDWORKING MUM

Our mum is tired
Our mum is stressed
Our mum works hard
What she'd like best
Is a day to rest
A day – just one
To be herself
And not be Mum
But we love her so!
And so she must
Suffer Mother's
Day with us!

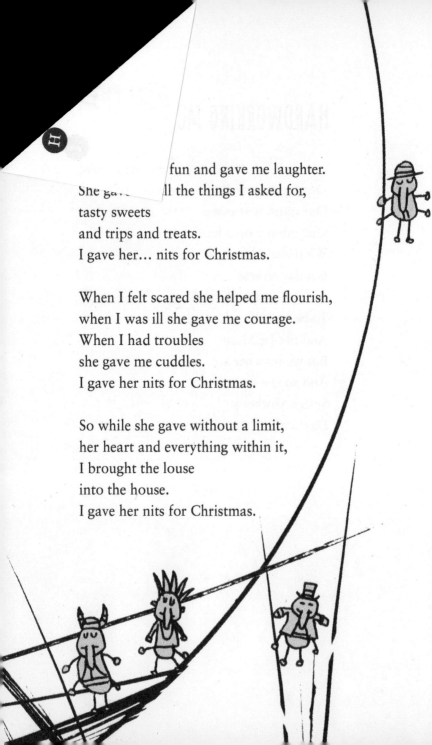

fun and gave me laughter.
She ga... ll the things I asked for,
tasty sweets
and trips and treats.
I gave her... nits for Christmas.

When I felt scared she helped me flourish,
when I was ill she gave me courage.
When I had troubles
she gave me cuddles.
I gave her nits for Christmas.

So while she gave without a limit,
her heart and everything within it,
I brought the louse
into the house.
I gave her nits for Christmas.

The advice she gave, she gave with love.
I gave her lice that sucked her blood,
eggs that hatched
and made her scratch.
I gave her nits for Christmas

There were other gifts. I gave her germs
and once I gave her bottom-worms.
She thanked me – not,
but to top the lot,
I gave her nits. FOR CHRISTMAS.

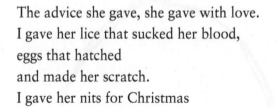

JUMP-ROPE MUM

42

A **1, 2, 3, 4, 5** and **6,**
Mum will show you how to skip.
She rides the highs, she rides the dips,
faster, faster, ever so quick.

Mum will show you how to skip,
she has the skills, she knows the tricks.
Heel – toe – swish – flick,
faster, faster, ever so quick.

Mum will show you how to skip,
no ifs no buts no slips no trips.
A **6, 5, 4, 3, 2** and **1,**
Let's hear it now for... Jump-Rope Mum!

Up with the early birds
Up with the sun
Everybody keep up with Keep-Fit Mum

SQUAT JUMP
CHEST THUMP
STAR JUMP
FIST PUMP
INHALE
EXHALE
SHOULDER PRESS
RUN

KEEP-FIT MUM

LEG LIFT
RUSSIAN TWIST
ROPE-SKIP
FLUTTER-KICK
GET-SET
ARMS-STRETCH
LEGS, BUM, TUM

Tra-la-la
Rum-tiddle-um
Everybody keep up
With Keep-Fit Mum

PILATES
KARATE
SYNERGY
TAI-CHI
HOOLA-HOOP
ZUMBA GROUP
It keeps you young

HIKING
CYCLING
KUNG-FU
FIGHTING
ACROBATICS
ACQUABATICS
Isn't this fun?

Tra-la-la
Rum-tiddle-um
Everybody keep up
Keep up, keep up
Everybody keep up
With Keep-Fit Mum

LUCKY MUMMY

I love my lucky mummy, I take her everywhere
And I wave my lucky mummy in the air

She's with me when I work
She's with me when I play
My mummy's always clapping
Everything I say

When I have exams
I hide her in my jumper
If I'm stuck on any sums
She whispers me the answer

I love my lucky mummy, I take her everywhere
And I wave my lucky mummy in the air

She comes to every match
She watches every race
And when my lucky mummy's there
I always come first place

But if I should fall over
And maybe graze my knee
My mummy will come running
to tend my injury
(AND CURSE THE REFEREE!)

Oh I love my lucky mummy, I take her everywhere
And I wave my lucky mummy in the air

Even though I'm 47... my mummy's always there
And I wave my lucky mummy
I wave my lucky mummy
I WAVE MY LUCKY MUMMY IN THE AIR!

MAGIC MUM

Who is this moonlit **M**idnight magician?
What gentle fairy **O**r conscientious goblin
Steals unseen through **T**he deadly bedlam of my bedroom?
And while I dream **H**appily of lands Elysian
Every night this most **E**nchanting apparition
Restores my unruly **R**oom to hallowed heaven

MEERKAT MOTHER

I think I've discovered why Mum is so small
Yet stands on her toes to try to be tall
Why she has a large nose and crescent-shaped ears that
She can close if she has to... she must be a meerkat

When we go to the seaside, she stays on dry land
Keeps an eye on the sky and digs up the sand
Why's she so jumpy? Is it because of her fear that
We'll be eaten by eagles? Or seagulls? Yes – she's a
   meerkat!

Why else would she enjoy so much sun on her belly?
Or find watching from windows more fun than the telly?
There's always some business she just has to peer at
Why is she so nosy? It's because she's a meerkat

My mother's a meerkat, she's really a meerkat
I know that it's weird when I think of the years that
I thought she was human and I had no idea that
She was some sort of mongoose – in fact she's a meerkat!

THE NEE-NAW MUMMY

Everyday our Nee-Naw Mummy saves us from disaster
Sometimes in her ambulance she comes to bring a plaster
Sometimes in her fire truck she comes to douse the flames
And often in her police car brings order to our games
But however Nee-Naw Mummy comes she's always in a hurry
Nee-naw nee-naw nee-naw goes our
  Nee-Naw Nee-Naw Mummy

THE NO-NO MUMMY

"No, no," says the No-No Mummy
"No, no, child, that's naughty."
No no no no no no no
Is what No-No Mummy's taught me
So when after tea she says to me
"Now up to bed you go!"
I sulk instead and shake my head
And tell No-No Mummy, "No!"

THE NIGHT-NIGHT MUMMY

The Night-Night Mummy says "Night-Night
It's time now for your sleepies…"
And as you sleep, off she creeps
To eat up all your sweeties.

ONE-HUNDRED-MILES-AN-HOUR MOTHER

My one-hundred-miles-an-hour mother
Kicks up more dust than the Roadrunner
Rushing to meet her every deadline
From home to work and back for bedtime
Like a swirling whirlwind, she's so busy
Just watching her makes you feel dizzy
I hope one day she gets to slow down
Drink her tea, watch a TV programme
Round in circles like this poem
Till then I guess she must keep going

MUMMA OPERA

When she sings in the morning, it shakes us awake
She sings in soprano and the windows all break

MUMMA OP-OP-OP-ER-AAAAA!

She sings down the street and she sings on the bus
Then wonders why people keep staring at us

MUMMA OP-OP-OP-ER-AAAAA!

She sings high and low and oh so dramatic
She waves both her arms and the pigeons all panic

MUMMA OP-OP-OP-ER-AAAAA!

When she hits her crescendo it gives us the shivers
Then she takes a bow and we throw her our knickers

MUMMA OP-OP-OP-ER-AAAAA!

She had a sore throat so she went to the doctor
He prescribed her the world's biggest gobstopper

But it still didn't stop her

MUMMA OP-OP-OP-ER
MUMMA OP-OP-OP-ER
MUMMA
   OP-OP-OP-ER- AAAAAAAAAA!

Ⓟ POKÉ-MOM

A Mum who speaks the
Japanese of Pokémon –

The ultimate rare

PROUD MUM

Hey, Mum, look at me. I'm on top of the world
I've climbed up so high and I hope that you're proud

I can walk, I can talk, I can skip, I can bounce
I can draw, I can read, I can write, I can count

I can swim, I can swing, I can sing, I can smile
I'm the boss, I can floss. Oh, look at my style

I'm one smart, happy-hearted, cool cartwheeling kid
Hey, Mum! Look at me. See what you did!

I'M THE HONEY MUMMY, ME
I'M NO COMMON POLLEN BEE
I'M THE HONEY MUMMY BEE
QUEEN OF THE COLONY

There's no beebread in my belly
I was raised on royal jelly
And I don't collect the pollen
For I'm not a bee who's common

QUEEN-BEE MUM

I DO NOT MAKE THE HONEY
BUT I AM THE HONEY MUMMY
I'M THE MUMMY TO THE HIVE
AND I KEEP THE HIVE ALIVE

Yes, I'm the Queen
There is no King
And I'm the only bee
Who can sting and sting and sting

I'M THE HONEY MUMMY, ME
I'M NO COMMON POLLEN BEE
I'M THE HONEY MUMMY BEE
QUEEN OF THE COLONY

The day that I flew free
All the boy bees followed me
We danced up in the sky
But then they had to die

FOR I DID NOT NEED A DRONE

SO I CAME HOME ALONE

AND I MADE THIS HIVE MY OWN

WITH MY REGAL PHEROMONE

Yes, I'm the Queen
There is no King
So feed me for you need me
And then listen to me sing

I'M THE HONEY MUMMY, ME

I'M NO COMMON POLLEN BEE

I'M THE HONEY MUMMY BEE

QUEEN OF THE COLONY

And all the eggs I lay
In their thousands every day
They keep this hive alive
And they help the world survive

RINGMASTER MUM

Mother is the star of the FAMOUS
CARTWHEEL FAMILY CIRCUS

She is the **RINGMASTER**

"Young Ladies and Gentlemen,
welcome to the show!
Take a ringside seat, tea is on the table!"

She is the **TRAPEZE ARTIST**

"Using my death-defying
powers of dexterity, I will
now attempt to walk barefoot
through your bedroom...
Drum Roll, please..."

She is the **STRONGWOMAN**

"Behold, as I lift a tired toddler onto my shoulders while carrying three bags of shopping, two cuddly toys, and a freshly painted portrait of Mr Potato Head…"

She is the **LION-TAMER**

"Leo! Stop roaring and chew your dinner quietly like a good little pussy-cat!"

She is the **FIRE-JUGGLER**

"Watch me juggle three after-school clubs, two arguments, the dog's dinner and a burning apple pie, before your very eyes!"

And she is the **CLOWN**

"Hello, Boys and Girls! No, these are not my pyjamas. Today I'm Boo-Hoo the Clown and I will be pulling a series of ridiculous faces to make your baby brother giggle…"

Yes, Mother is the star of the FAMOUS CARTWHEEL FAMILY CIRCUS –

RINGMASTER, TRAPEZE ARTIST, STRONGWOMAN, LION-TAMER, FIRE-JUGGLER and **CLOWN.**

Wow – she's clever!

And yet listen to the crowd...

No applause whatsoever.

THE SCHOOL-RUN MUM

(after Da Doo Ron Ron by Barry/Greenwich/Spector)

You see her in the morning at a half-past eight
The School-Run Mum, oh the School-Run Mum
She's got her foot right down cos she can't be late
The School-Run Mum, oh the School-Run Mum

Yeah, at a half past-eight!
Yeah, she can't be late!
She's singing this song as she drives along
The School-Run Mum, oh the School-Run Mum

She's got to be first to get to the gate
The School-Run Mum, oh the School-Run Mum
Then she's gotta work, she got a lot on her plate
The School-Run Mum, oh the School-Run Mum

Yeah, she got to get to the gate!
Yeah, she got a lot on her plate!
The Lollipop Man he just waves her on
The School-Run Mum, oh the School-Run Mum

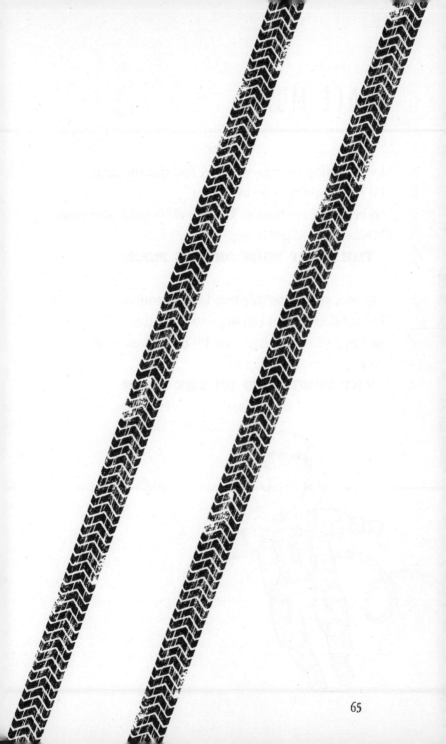

SPACE MUM

I was tidying your toys when I had this thought
I'd really rather be an astronaut
So beam me up, Scotty! You can clean your own room
While I float about being
THE FIRST MUM ON THE MOON

My son, you're the star that I orbit around
But if I don't refuel I shall go to ground
So I'm packing my bags and I'll be back as soon
As I've planted my flag as
THE FIRST MUM ON THE MOON

All that time and space to ponder
They say distance makes the heart grow fonder
Such tranquillity and so much wonder
To see... up on the moon

I've been so busy since I gave birth
I don't think there will ever be peace on Earth
So, let's start the countdown...
   3, 2, 1, ZOOM
Wave to me. I'll be on TV –
   THE FIRST MUM ON THE MOON!

STUNT MOTHER

Who's in a race against the clock
All because her son forgot
His raincoat and his packed-lunch box?
STUNT MOTHER!

Who jumps the fences, scales the gates
Swims shark-infested seas and lakes
Sprints after cars and overtakes?
STUNT MOTHER!

Who rides her bike through burning flames?
Surfs the roofs of hurtling trains?
Clings on to wings of aeroplanes?
STUNT MOTHER!

While her son sits helpless in his lessons
As his tummy rumbles and rain clouds threaten
Who'll be back before the lunch-bell beckons?
STUNT MOTHER!

And now with the coat and lunch retrieved
(One from a cupboard plagued with beasts
The other pulled from her bulldog's teeth)
STUNT MOTHER!

Rides the rapids in her kayak
Then barebacks on a horse she's hijacked
Galloping towards the final climax
STUNT MOTHER!

Sees her son still locked in limbo
With one last leap, her legs akimbo
Crashes through the classroom window
STUNT MOTHER!

Has saved her son from hunger pains
And from the pelt of thunder-rains
See how the headlines praise her name
STUNT MOTHER!

She sneers at fear. Nothing stops her
She does not care what her love costs her
Someone please give her an Oscar
So Ladies and Gentlemen let's hear it
one more time for...
STUNT MOTHER!

TREE MUM

Seasons come
Seasons go
Sunshine, rain
Sleet and snow
Leaves fall down
Flowers grow
Years disappear
And still tears flow

In the woodland
By the cemetery
Together as
A family
We gather by our
'Mother Tree'
We planted in
Mum's memory

We nurture her
As she nurtured us
Dressed and fed
And watered us
We talk to her
Like she talked to us
Share our laughter
Love and loss

Seasons come
Seasons go
Sunshine, rain
Sleet and snow
Healing time
Ticks too slow
We tend our tree
And see it grow

And often by
Our Mother Tree
I feel Mum here
And know she'll be
Part of us and
Part of me
In our hearts
For all eternity

TWO MUMS

It took two mums to take me to school every day,
one mum for each hand and I'd swing all the way.

It took two mums to show me
there's more than one way of living,
that you can walk with the crowd
or be proud to be different.

It took two mums to soothe me when I was sick,
to take turns to nurse me until I felt fit.

It took two mums to tell me
there's more than one way of seeing,
how one person's jail
to another is freedom.

And when the bullies came knocking and I was afraid,
it took two mums to help me stand up and be brave.

It took two mums to teach me
not to tease or to judge.
I have two mums to love me
so there's two mums I love.

UNDERCOVER-SPY MOTHER

Shhh! Fingers on lips
I'll whisper you why
I've discovered my mother is
... an undercover spy.

She tells everybody she's a telephone operative for BT
But I know that's not quite the whole truth
And I've got good reason to suspect
My mum's really a professional snoop
Connected to a top-secret underground network
Called... Mumsnet!

Last night
I crept out of bed
And caught her up on the computer
Spreading classified intelligence
(Everything I've done and said!)
To foreign agents
Across the world-wide web

And she's hired other eyes to spy on me as well...
The dinner lady
Checking I've eaten all my peas...
She's a spy

My class teacher
Scribbling coded messages
Into the register
He's a spy

And as for Grandma
She swears she's not...
But what very big eyes she's got!

Still, I'm getting wise to all my mum's tricks and disguises
And all her prying enterprises will soon be exposed
BIG TIME!

Because
Shhh! Fingers on lips!
No word of a lie
I've discovered
My mother is an undercover spy

But surprise, surprise, Mother

So... am... I !

UNIVERSAL MUM

If I had to choose one
Universal language
It would be Mother Tongue

All around the world you hear how M is for Mum,
Mom, Ma, Mę, Matka, Majka, Maja,
Mare, Mère, Máthair, Mëmë, Mati, Mātā, Mada,
Mána, Mamma, Manman, Moeder, Mutter,
Mor, Madre, Mortina, Maminka

Though sometimes you might hear
Umm, Ema, Ama, Ina, Nana, Ibu, Haha or Tina

But mostly Mother Tongue speaks without words
And is seen in smiles or heard
In squeaks, squeals, chirps
Barks, howls, growls or whistles
Or sent with scent and smelt
Or felt with cuddles, licks and kisses

M, MOM, MA, ME, MATKA, MAJKA, MAJA, MARE,

In cities and villages
Deserts, oceans, jungles and forests
All over this planet
One way or another
All of us creatures speak our Mother Tongue
And Mother Love's a language understood by everyone

MUTTER, MOEDER, MANAM, MAMAN, MAMMA, MÁNA, MADA, MATA, MATI, MÉMË, MÁTHAIR, RE, MOR, MADRE, MORTINA, MAMINA, RA

VOYAGER MUM

Our Voyager Mum has left once more for sea.
All my fiercest screams could not prevent her.
I hope she will be back in time for tea.

The rain pours. The wind blows so bitterly,
but though I've warned her of the bad weather
our Voyager Mum has left once more for sea.

Nan's here. She's nice. Yet both of us agree
when Mum's home with me it's so much better.
I hope she will be back in time for tea.

And while I sit inside and watch TV,
a pirate dreaming of wild adventure,
our Voyager Mum has left once more for sea.

What if she's lost and can't sail back to me?
What if she's gone, I mean gone forever?
I hope she will be back in time for tea.

Nan says, "Because there is no 'money tree'
and so someone has to search for treasure,
your Voyager Mum has left once more for sea."

I hope she will be back in time for tea.

WINDRUSH MUM

The war was over. But for my dad and my mum
life remained hard on the land they were from.
They'd fought for our freedom and now they were free
to answer the call of the **Mother Country**.

So Dad sold his chickens, his pigs and the goat.
He bought us the tickets. We boarded the boat.
I was only a baby when we sailed across the sea
and into the arms of the **Mother Country**.

Later they told me, "She wouldn't look in our eyes.
We were her children she didn't quite recognise."
But still we sang, 'London is the place for me!'
And we sang it with pride for the **Mother Country**.

She turned quickly bitter and as cold as her frost,
and sometimes she treated us worse than her dogs.
Though her curses cut deep we kept our dignity
and we all kept our faith in the **Mother Country**.

Dad drove her buses and he carried her bricks,
Mum worked in her hospitals nursing the sick.
Each task that she asked of them they did honestly,
and all for the love of the **Mother Country**.

And when I grew up I too went to work,
first as her cleaner and then as her clerk,
and soon I was blessed with my own family,
all raised on respect for the **Mother Country**.

And now that I'm old and my work is all done
she tells me to go back to where I came from.
But I am her daughter, not her enemy,
And I've no other home than the **Mother Country**.

After all I have loved and all that I've laboured,
After all that I gave and all I forgave her,
Why now should she question my lifelong loyalty?
Oh, where is the love of the Mother for me?

The 'Mother Country' in this poem is Great Britain. After World War Two, the British government gave citizens of its colonies the right to settle in the United Kingdom. Between 1948 and 1970 nearly half a million people moved from a variety of different Commonwealth countries to Britain, with some of the first Caribbean migrants arriving on a ship called the Empire Windrush.

From November 2017 newspapers began to report that some of these migrants, who had full legal rights to be in the UK, had been threatened with being sent back to their countries of birth, or had already been deported. No matter that (like the character in this poem) many had only been babies or children at the time of migration, and had spent almost all of their lives working, making friends and raising families in the UK.

WORD OF MUM

Ask all the daughters and the sons
what was the first word on their tongue?
The word that's cried and sighed and sung.
Mum's the word. The word is Mum.

Are you feeling lonely, lost or glum?
Got a breaking heart? An aching tum?
A sore throat? A teething gum?
Mum's the word. The word is Mum.

The word is hurled, the word is hummed,
the word is wailed, the word is drummed,
with all the breath left in our lungs
Mum's the word. The word is Mum

Have your laces come undone?
D'you need someone to quickly come
to help you with a tricky sum?
And what's that word you've stumbled on?

We can't keep it secret. We can't keep *schtum*.
Mum's the word. The word is Mum.

X-RAY-EYE MUM

My mother has got x-ray eyes
And they can see the truth
Whatever I do she's not surprised
My mother has got x-ray eyes
They shine their light on all my lies
One glare lays bare the proof
My mother has got x-ray eyes
And they can see the truth

XMAS MUM (MOTHER CHRISTMAS)

I check the list once and I check the list twice
And I know who is naughty and I know who is nice
But who helps the elves
To stock up the shelves
And ensures we have all the supplies?

Who tends to my beard? Who mends my old boots?
Who joins up the dots when she plots out my route?
Who doubles my size
With her tasty mince pies
Then squeezes me into my suit?

Who mucks out the reindeer,
    packs the sleigh for the flight?
Shines up Rudolf's nose so it glows really bright?
Who keeps my cheeks rosy
And the grotto all cosy
And tucks those elves into bed every night?

Who puts the laugh in my heart and the glint in my wink?
Runs my Christmas Day bath and pours me a drink?
And who will not have it
When I say she's the magic?

Who? Well, who do you think?

YOUNG MOTHER

Dear Fairy Godmother,

My name is Ella and I am 12. I'm writing to you
as I don't know anyone else who can help.

You see, sometimes, I feel like I'm living at
the beginning of a fairytale. The bit before you
come in with your magic spell. The part where
the heroine is lonely, and her life feels like hell,
until you appear and wave your wand to make
everything end well.

Don't get me wrong, it's not like I'm
CINDER-ella. I adore my family and hope we
can stay together. My sisters are a handful but
they're beautiful not ugly. And my mum is never
ever cruel, she really really loves me. She's ill,
that's all, and there's not much she can do. So I
look after her and my young sisters too.

I'm not writing to ask for a new dress. Or –
yuck! – for a prince to make me his princess.
There's only one wish I really wish would come
true and I know that's beyond the power of
even a fairy like you. Though if my mum ever did
get better, I think all of my family would live
happily forever.

But, for now, I thought I'd write this letter
as best I can. It helps to know that somewhere
there is someone who understands when I say
that some days I feel too young to play the
mum, and I wish I could... just have some fun.

Love from your biggest fan ever,

Ella.

ZZZZ MOTHER

If I should sleep before you do
Sing this song I sing for you
This song I sing that soothes your cry
My sleepy-baby lullaby....

If I should sleep before you sleep
Know my love is diamond deep
Diamond deep and airplane high
My love for you could touch the sky

Could touch the sky! And hush the wind!
Could still a storm and make it sing
A song as gentle as a stream
And dance you dizzy to your dream

To your dream to dance! And though I know
The time will come to let you go
To let you go and set you free
My love for you will always be

It will always be! Not only when
The day dawns light and bright again
But in the dark and dreamy deep
When you close your eyes and go to sleep

So, If I should sleep before you do
Sing this song I sing for you
This song I sing that soothes your cry
My sleepy-Mummy lullaby....

ABOUT JUSTIN COE

 Justin Coe is a performance poet on a mission to reconnect people with poetry and poetry with people. A regular and popular performer in schools, theatres and community settings, he has entertained everywhere from Sheppey to Shanghai and from the Savoy Hotel to street corners, steam trains and a sitting-room made entirely out of newspaper.

In the last decade, since re-locating to Southend and becoming a father, Justin has written and toured nine spoken-word theatre shows for young people. Recent work has included *Big Wow Small Wonder*, *Young Herbert's Horrors* (both with Half Moon Theatre) and his interactive stand-up poetry show *Are We Being Silly?* His brand new show *The House That Jackson Built* will be touring nationwide from March 2020.

For more information about Justin's poetry, theatre shows and school and library visits, please visit www.justincoe.co.uk

ABOUT STEVE WELLS

 Steve Wells is a Bath-based designer and illustrator. He works for lots of publishers, including Chicken House, Scholastic, Mills and Boon and Harper Collins. He has designed over 300 book covers and his spontaneous and scratchy illustrations have appeared in more than a dozen books. His illustrations have been published around the world. He lives in Bath with his wife and one cat and is the proud father to three children.

You can see more of his work on his website: stevewellsdesign.com or on Instagram at: @mrs.cats_life

Also Available from Otter-Barry Books

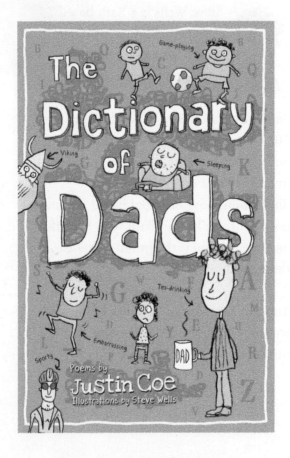

"A fantastic book that gathers together
just about every type of dad you can
think of in a brilliant poetry A-Z."
Read It Daddy

The Dictionary of Dads
ISBN 978-1-91095-916-9